1965

Merry Christmas
from
Grandma + Dexter
Grandpa

Little Town
of Bethlehem

Also by Hertha Pauli

SILENT NIGHT
LINCOLN'S LITTLE CORRESPONDENT
THREE IS A FAMILY
BERNADETTE AND THE LADY
CHRISTMAS AND THE SAINTS
THE TWO TRUMPETERS OF VIENNA
THE FIRST EASTER RABBIT
THE FIRST CHRISTMAS TREE
AMERICA'S FIRST CHRISTMAS

Little Town of Bethlehem

By HERTHA PAULI

Illustrated by Fritz Kredel

DUELL, SLOAN AND PEARCE

New York

Copyright © 1963 by Hertha Pauli

All rights reserved. No part of this book
may be reproduced in any form without
permission in writing from the publisher.

First edition

Library of Congress Catalogue Card Number: 63-16847

Duell,
Sloan
&Pearce

Affiliate of
MEREDITH PRESS
Des Moines & New York

Manufactured in the United States of America

WHEN you hear the carols ring out at Christmastime, do you wonder about the story they are telling you?

It is the story of a wonderful birthday — the most beloved birthday story in the world. Each of our carols tells you a little more about it. Come along with a song, to a little town called Bethlehem:

> *O little town of Bethlehem,*
> How still we see thee lie!
> Above thy deep and dreamless sleep
> The silent stars go by.

Silently the stars look down on Bethlehem and on the hills around it. What a quiet little town it is, so calm in the peaceful night! It seems never to change, never to grow. The low houses always look dust-colored under their flat roofs. The crooked streets wind their way toward the fields outside the little town. Sheep still graze in these fields, and shepherds watch them just as they did in the times of the Bible.

It was in these fields, almost two thousand years ago, that our birthday story began:

While shep — herds watched their flocks by night, All
seat — ed on the ground, The an — gel of the
Lord came down, And glo — ry shone a — round.

At first, when the angel stood before them, the shepherds were very much afraid. But the angel spoke kindly to them. "Fear not," he said. "I bring you good tidings of great joy."

Then the shepherds forgot their fear, for they felt the glory of God all about them. Yes, even the sheep raised their woolly heads as if they, too, could understand the angel.

And the angel went on: "To you is born this day in the city of David a Saviour, who is Christ the Lord."

The shepherds knew that Bethlehem was called the city of David, because King David of Israel had been born there. But they did not know about a new-born Saviour.

"You shall find the babe wrapped in swaddling clothes, lying in a manger," said the angel.

And suddenly there were a great many angels around the first one, all praising God and singing!

Hark! the herald angels sing,
  "Glory to the new-born King!"

Then the angels returned to heaven, and the
stars alone shone in the silent night. Slowly the
shepherds began to talk about what they had
heard and seen.

"Let us now go to Bethlehem," said one.

"Let us see what the Lord has made known to us," said another.

And off they went with their flocks. They went in such a hurry that one small lamb was not able to follow. So a shepherd boy picked it up and carried it across his shoulders.

It was about two miles to Bethlehem, uphill through groves of olive and fig trees. Higher and higher the shepherds climbed with their flocks to reach the little town.

The angel had told them that the child would be lying in a manger. To the shepherds, of course, a manger was a familiar thing: it belonged in a stable and was filled with hay for the animals. But the shepherds had never seen a manger with a child in it! And how, they wondered, could a

king be born in a stable? The more they wondered, the less they could understand.

When they came to Bethlehem, they did not
know where to turn in the crooked streets. They
did not know where to start looking for the stable,
until suddenly they saw starlit tracks leading to a
cave in a hillside. A bright star shone upon the
narrow entrance, and by its light the shepherds

could see a stable inside. Was this the place? Excitedly they went in.

Inside, an ox and an ass stood watching the manger. A man and a woman knelt beside it. Their heads were bowed, their hands were folded. And lying in the manger was a child wrapped in swaddling clothes.

A— way in a man — ger, no crib for his

bed, The lit — tle Lord Je — sus laid

down his sweet head. The stars in the

sky —— looked down where he lay. The

lit — tle Lord Je — sus, a — sleep on the hay.

All knelt before the manger in adoration — the shepherds, the man, and the woman. *The friendly beasts* stood looking on in wonder. What was in their minds?

"I," said the don — key, shag — gy and brown. "I

car — ried His moth — er up hill and down, I

car — ried her safe — ly to Beth — le — hem town;

I," said the don — key, shag — gy and brown.

The mother's name was Mary. With her husband Joseph she had come from the city of Nazareth, where he was a carpenter. But the Roman Emperor had ordered all people to go to their home towns and register for their taxes. So Joseph and Mary had traveled all the way from Nazareth to Bethlehem, because this was the home of their family line, which began with David the King.

When they arrived in Bethlehem, there was no room for them at the inn. They found no room at all in the little town. The only place where they could stay was the stable they now shared with the ox and the ass. There Mary's little son was born. She called him Jesus and wrapped him in swaddling clothes. And because she had no crib to put him in, she laid him in the manger.

And now that the shepherds had seen the child in the manger, they understood what the angel had told them. Heavenly radiance filled the poor stable in that most wonderful night:

Si – lent night, ho – ly night, All is calm,
all is bright Round yon vir – gin moth–er and child.
Ho – ly in–fant so ten–der and mild, Sleep in heav – en – ly
peace, —— Sleep in heav – en – ly peace. ——

When the shepherds returned from Bethlehem, they told everyone what they had seen in the stable. And all who heard it marveled at their story. It has been told and retold ever since:

While shep-herds kept their watch-ing O'er si — lent flocks by night, Be-

-hold through—out the | hea—vens There | shone a ho — ly | light

ril.

REFRAIN:

Go, tell it on the | moun — tain, O — ver the hills and

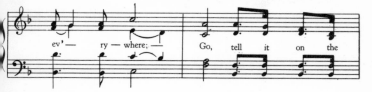

ev' — ry — where; — Go, tell it on the

moun'— tain That | Je — sus Christ is born! —

Today a great church stands where the Christ
Child was born. It is called the Church of the
Nativity. Many beautiful lamps are always

lighted around the birthplace, and a silver star
adorns the spot where Mary laid her Son in the
manger.

Each Christmas Day, people from all over the
world come to the great Church of the Nativity.
They come in processions, praising God and singing:

O come all ye faith — ful, joy — ful and tri —

— umph — ant, O come ye, O come —— ye to

Beth — le - hem; Come and be - hold him, born the King of an - gels; O come, let us a — dore him, O come, let us a - dore him, O come, let us a — dore him, — Christ, — the Lord!

His coming to earth meant so much that all our time is measured from the year when He was born, almost two thousand years ago. And year after year, on December 25th, we celebrate His birthday.

We light Christmas candles and trim the Christmas tree. We put little figures in the Christmas Crib: Mary and Joseph, the ox and the ass, and the shepherds with their sheep, adoring the Child in the manger, just as they did in the stable of Bethlehem.

And every year, on wings of song, the carols take you to the little town. You see the shepherds, watching their flocks by night, and you hear the angels sing their joyful message. Now, on this happiest birthday of all, let's join the choir:

Joy. to the world! the Lord is come: Let

earth re – ceive her King; — Let ev' – ry

heart — pre – pare — him — room, — And

heav'n and na – ture sing, And heav'n and na – ture
Let heav'n and na – ture sing, Let

sing, And heav–en, and heav—en and na – ture sing.
heav'n and na–ture sing.

O Little Town of Bethlehem

O little town of Bethlehem,
How still we see thee lie!
Above thy deep and dreamless sleep
The silent stars go by;
Yet in thy dark streets shineth
The everlasting Light;
The hopes and fears of all the years
Are met in thee tonight.

For Christ is born of Mary,
And gathered all above,
While mortals sleep, the angels keep
Their watch of wondering love.
O morning stars, together
Proclaim the holy birth!
And praises sing to God the King,
And peace to men on earth.

How silently, how silently,
The wondrous gift is given!
So God imparts to human hearts
The blessings of his heaven.
No ear may hear his coming,
But in this world of sin,
Where meek souls will receive him, still
The dear Christ enters in.

O holy Child of Bethlehem!
Descend to us, we pray;
Cast out our sin and enter in;
Be born in us today.
We hear the Christmas angels
The great glad tidings tell;
O come to us, abide with us,
Our Lord Emmanuel!

While Shepherds Watched
Their Flocks by Night

While shepherds watched their flocks by night,
All seated on the ground,
The angel of the Lord came down,
And glory shone around.

"Fear not," said he, for mighty dread
Had seized their troubled mind,
"Glad tidings of great joy I bring
To you and all mankind.

"To you, in David's town, this day
Is born of David's line
The Savior, who is Christ the Lord;
And this shall be the sign:

"The heavenly babe you there shall find
To human view displayed,
All meanly wrapped in swathing bands,
And in a manger laid."

Thus spake the seraph; and forthwith
Appeared a shining throng
Of angels praising God, who thus
Addressed their joyful song:

"All glory be to God on high
And to the earth be peace;
Good will henceforth from heaven to men
Begin and never cease."

Hark! the Herald Angels Sing

Hark! the herald angels sing,
"Glory to the new-born King;
Peace on earth, and mercy mild,
God and sinners reconciled!"
Joyful, all ye nations, rise,
Join the triumph of the skies;
With the angelic host proclaim,
"Christ is born in Bethlehem!"
    REFRAIN: Hark! the herald angels sing,
                "Glory to the new-born King!"

Christ, by highest heaven adored;
Christ, the ever-lasting Lord!
Late in time behold him come,
Off-spring of the Virgin's womb.
Veiled in flesh the Godhead see;
Hail the incarnate Deity,
Pleased as man with men to dwell,
Jesus, our Emmanuel.   REFRAIN

Hail the heaven-born Prince of peace!
Hail the Sun of righteousness!
Light and life to all he brings,
Risen with healing in his wings,
Mild he lays his glory by,
Born that man no more may die,
Born to raise the sons of earth,
Born to give them second birth.   REFRAIN

Away in a Manger

Away in a manger, no crib for his bed,
The little Lord Jesus laid down his sweet head.
The stars in the sky looked down where he lay.
The little Lord Jesus, asleep on the hay.

The cattle are lowing, the baby awakes,
But little Lord Jesus, no crying he makes.
I love thee, Lord Jesus, look down from the sky,
And stay by my cradle till morning is nigh.

Be near me, Lord Jesus; I ask thee to stay
Close by me forever, and love me, I pray.
Bless all the dear children in thy tender care,
And fit us for heaven, to live with thee there.

The Friendly Beasts

Jesus our brother, kind and good,
Was humbly born in a stable rude,
And the friendly beasts around Him stood;
Jesus our brother, kind and good.

"I," said the donkey, shaggy and brown.
"I carried His mother up hill and down,
I carried her safely to Bethlehem town;
I," said the donkey, shaggy and brown.

"I," said the cow, all white and red,
"I gave Him my manger for His bed,
I gave Him my hay to pillow His head;
I," said the cow, all white and red.

"I," said the sheep, with the curly horn,
"I gave Him my wool for His blanket warm;
He wore my coat on Christmas morn.
I," said the sheep with the curly horn.

"I," said the dove, from the rafters high,
"Cooed Him to sleep, my mate and I,
We cooed Him to sleep, my mate and I,
I," said the dove, from the rafters high.

And every beast, by some good spell,
In the stable dark, was glad to tell,
Of the gift he gave Emmanuel,
The gift he gave Emmanuel.

Silent Night, Holy Night

Silent night, holy night,
All is calm, all is bright
Round yon virgin mother and child.
Holy infant so tender and mild,
Sleep in heavenly peace,
Sleep in heavenly peace.

Silent night, holy night,
Shepherds quake at the sight,
Glories stream from heaven afar,
Heavenly hosts sing alleluia;
Christ, the Savior, is born!
Christ, the Savior, is born!

Silent night, holy night,
Son of God, love's pure light
Radiant beams from thy holy face,
With the dawn of redeeming grace,
Jesus, Lord, at thy birth,
Jesus, Lord at thy birth.

Go, Tell It on the Mountain

REFRAIN: Go, tell it on the mountain,
     Over the hills and everywhere;
     Go, tell it on the mountain
     That Jesus Christ is born!

While shepherds kept their watching
O'er silent flocks by night,
Behold throughout the heavens
There shone a holy light. REFRAIN

The shepherds feared and trembled
When lo! above the earth
Rang out the angel chorus
That hailed our Savior's birth. REFRAIN

Down in a lowly manger
The humble Christ was born,
And God sent us salvation
That blessed Christmas morn. REFRAIN

O Come, All Ye Faithful

O come all ye faithful, joyful and triumphant,
O come ye, O come ye to Bethlehem;
Come and behold him, born the King of angels;
   REFRAIN: O come, let us adore him,
          O come, let us adore him,
          O come, let us adore him,
          Christ, the Lord!

Sing, choirs of angels, sing in exultation,
Sing, all ye citizens of heaven above!
Glory to God, all glory in the highest;   REFRAIN

Child, for us sinners poor and in the manger,
We would embrace thee, with love and awe;
Who would not love thee, loving us so dearly? REFRAIN

Yea, Lord, we greet thee, born this happy morning,
Jesus, to thee be all glory given;
Word of the Father, now in flesh appearing; REFRAIN

Joy to the World! the Lord is Come

Joy to the world! the Lord is come:
Let earth receive her King;
Let every heart prepare him room,
And heaven and nature sing,
And heaven and nature sing,
And heaven, and heaven and nature sing,

Joy to the earth! the Savior reigns:
Let men their songs employ;
While fields and floods, rocks, hills, and plains
Repeat the sounding joy,
Repeat the sounding joy,
Repeat, repeat the sounding joy.

He rules the world with truth and grace,
And makes the nations prove
The glories of his righteousness,
And wonders of his love,
And wonders of his love,
And wonders, wonders of his love.